Chapter 1

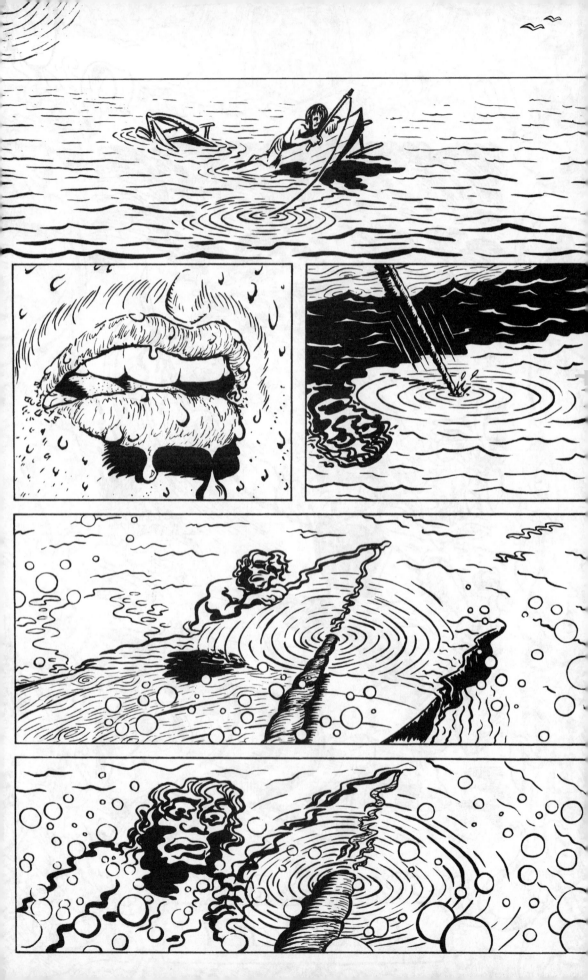

KRAK-OW!

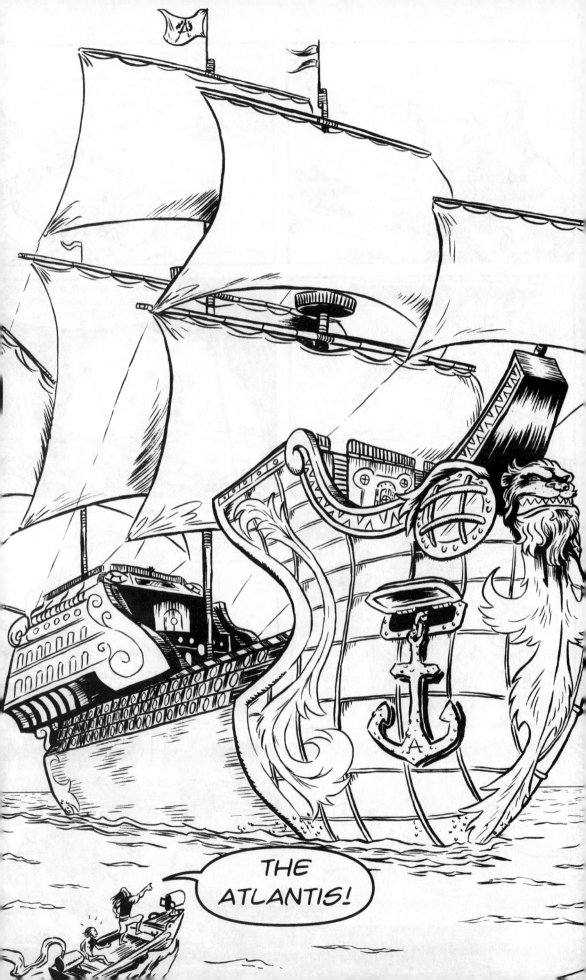

YAHHH!

BARK!

AS I WAS SAYING, ASTACIDAE—ENPHANTAS MOVE IN SCHOOLS AND CAN TRACK FOOD AT GREAT DISTANCES.

THEY ARE, HOW—EVER, INCAPABLE OF TRAVERSING THOSE DISTANCES THEMSELVES.

BLAM

HOW THEN, CAN THE SCHOOL MOVE SO MANY LEAGUES WITH GREAT SPEED?

THE ANSWER, OF COURSE, IS QUITE SIMPLE.

BLAM

THEY CATCH A RIDE....

I JUST NEED TO GET THE AUTO-LOADER FOR THE MAIN BATTERY UP AND RUNNING.

KEEP THEM OFF THE BATTLE-BRIDGE, LAD.

I ONLY NEED ANOTHER MOMENT!

ROOAAH!

ASTACIDAE-ENPHANTAS FOLLOW THE FOOD SUPPLY.

SO LET'S GIVE THEM...

HA HA! WE DID IT!

HUNGER TRUMPS SENSE FOR THESE CANNIBALS AND WE'VE TURNED IT AGAINST THEM!

NOW LET'S GET US AWAY...

...BEFORE THEY FINISH THEIR FEAST.

Chapter 2

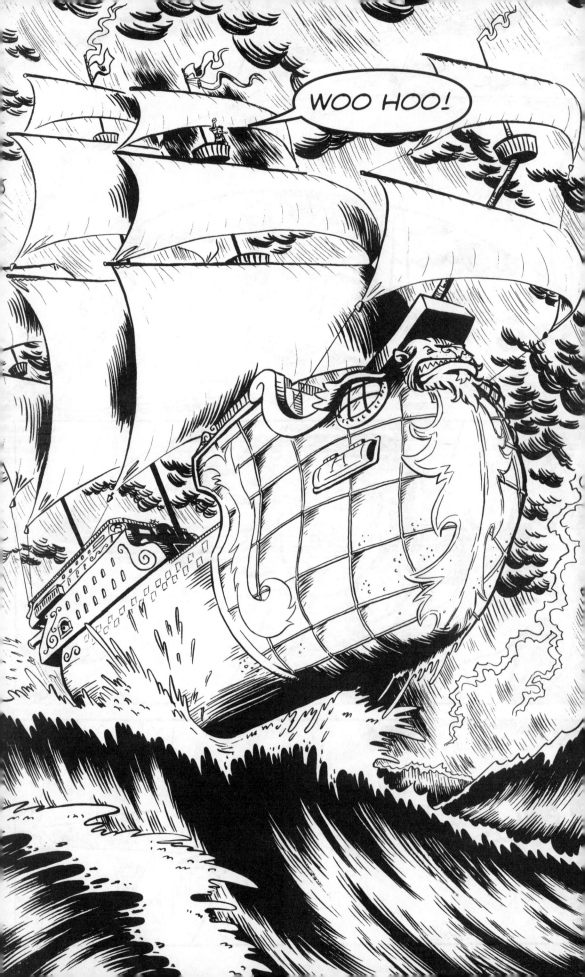

NAAHH!
TARTUS—LO!

EDWARD...

---WE LEAVE.

AHH!

PLEASE, I KNOW HOW THIS LOOKS.

IT LOOKS HORRIFIC.

BUT I WAS TRYING TO SAVE HER, I NEVER MEANT——

VO-CROM TEM, LO-SAR VO LAM!

MASE BO.

MO LAMAN BRAN KEELO BRANA.

I TRIED TO SAVE HER.

I TRULY DID.

HEEM COLO BARR!

IT JUST DOESN'T MAKE ANY SENSE.

HE COULDN'T HAVE KNOWN THE GIRL, CHOSOT'S NEVER VISITED THESE WATERS.

HE SAID SO HIMSELF.

UNLESS THAT WAS JUST ANOTHER LIE.

GOD, FOWLER, DO YOU EVEN KNOW THIS MAN?

YOU FIND A MAN FLOATING IN THE SEA AND DON'T BOTHER TO QUESTION HOW HE GOT THERE?

LO-AMAN!

HOW COULD YOU BE SO BLIND TO HIS...

BLIND INDEED, FOWLER.

YOU FIND A MAN FLOATING IN THE SEA...

...AND DON'T BOTHER TO QUESTION HOW HE GOT THERE.

JO—MACT!

UFFF!

DO YOU EXPECT ME TO BEG FOR MY LIFE?

TO SCREAM AND CRY?

WELL, ADJUST YOUR EXPECTATIONS!

VANDRAN COMAN TIE!

IF YOU'RE SO FOCUSED ON KILLING ME THAT MEANS YOU'RE NOT LOOKING FOR CHOSOT.

AND IF MY DEATH FREES HIM FROM YOU WRETCHED SLAVERS THAT'S A DEATH I CAN LIVE WITH.

I CAN DIE FOR A FRIEND.

KRA-KOW!

THAT ONE HAS MY RIFLE.

Chapter 3

ALDAN TOMM!

...PLAN.

WRRRRRRR

UM--- HELLO.

I'M DOCTOR JULIUS FOWLER, ACTING CAPTAIN OF HER MAJESTY'S FAR-SEA EXPLORATION VESSEL THE ATLANTIS.

CHOSOT TELLS ME THAT YOUR TRIBE ARE REFERRED TO AS THE TLOTLIN.

I'M STILL PUZZLING OUT YOUR TONGUE, DOES TLOTLIN TRANSLATE TO--

NO, DON'T BE AFRAID, SIR!

I MEAN NO HARM!

TRULY, MY BEST FRIEND IS TLOTLIN!

EEEEE

WHAT NOW?

MAROSO?

DOCTOR FOWLER LEM CON-VO SENI.

YOU SAY THAT THE ISLE YOU HAIL FROM IS HIDDEN.

IF SO, HOW WOULD YOU FIND IT AGAIN WHEN YOU WENT OUT TO HARVEST?

TRANSLATE THAT, LAD.

MAROSO, VO-TORO LAGO MASAT CON-TAGO.

VO-NOM RENIN AGON SEMSA VO-LAMA REETO?

IT'S THE STARS, CORRECT?

A SECRET PATH BURIED IN THE CONSTELLA-TIONS.

YOU'VE BEEN STAR-ING AT THAT PATCH OF SKY YOUR WHOLE LIFE, JUST WAITING TO ONE DAY FOLLOW IT HOME.

IT'S TIME NOW, GREAT-MOTHER.

IT'S TIME TO GO HOME.

TELL HER, CHOSOT.

TELL HER WHAT I SAID.

Concept Art

To realize the world of *Doctor Atlantis*, Ian and I have endless conversations about the aesthetic scheme. We go over technology, costumes, the degree of historical accuracy and how much we can just make up. In the end though, it all comes down to sitting at the desk and putting it on paper.

Here's an example of what those conversations end up looking like on the page.

-Carl Mefferd

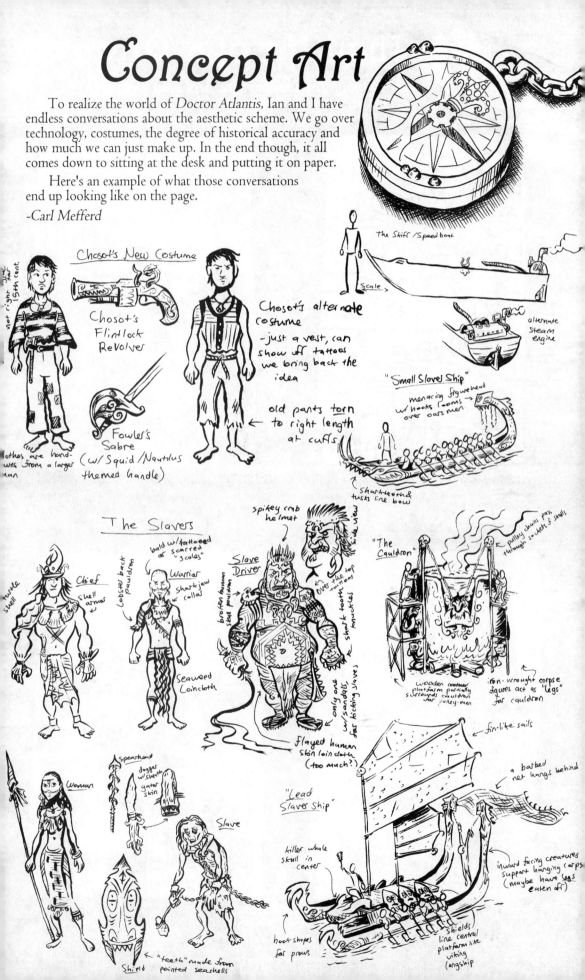

the Skiff / Speed boat

scale

alternate steam engine

Chosot's New Costume

Chosot's Flintlock Revolver

Fowler's Sabre (w/ Squid /Nautilus themed handle)

not right for 15th cent.

clothes are hand-wns from a larger man

Chosot's alternate costume
- just a vest, can show off tattoos we bring back the idea

old pants torn to right length at cuffs

"Small Slaver Ship"

menacing figurehead w/ hooks looms over oarsmen

shark-teeth & tusks line bow

The Slavers

turtle shell

Chief

shell armor

spikey crab helmet

bald w/ tattooed or scarred "scales"

Lobster-back Pauldron

Warrior

Shark-jaw collar

Seaweed Loincloth

Slave Driver

broken human skull pauldron

over the top tattoos

side view

shark tooth knuckles

only one w/ sandals for kicking slaves

flayed human skin loin cloth (too much?)

"The Cauldron"

pulley chains pass through sockets & skulls

wooden platform partially surrounds cauldron for pulley-men

iron-wrought corpse figures act as "legs" for cauldron

Woman

spearhead

dagger w/ sheath gator skin

Slave

"Lead Slaver Ship"

killer whale skull in center

hook shapes for prows

"teeth" made from pointed seashells

Shield

fin-like sails

a barbed net hangs behind

inward facing creatures support hanging corpse (maybe have legs eaten off)

shields line central platform like viking longship

The Life of a Page

Every page for Doctor Atlantis goes through several steps in its creation. Here's an example from page 18 of Chapter 2.

Thumbnails:
In the earliest step I make a tiny (often 2"x3") sketch based on Ian's script. At this stage I figure out the panel layout and general image. They look messy and doodly, but thumbnails are often the most important step in making comics.

Roughs:
Next, I loosely sketch the art at 6"x9" on printer paper. Here I make the image more specific and focus on strong composition. This page is then scanned, enlarged to 11"x17" and printed out.

Finished Pencils:
Using a lightbox, I trace the enlarged rough pencils in blue pencil lead on 11"x17" bristol board. As I trace I'll tighten the lines and add fine details.

Inks:
Finally, I ink my finished pencils with a sable brush and India Ink. I'll also use dip and tech pens for especially thin or mechanical lines. After scanning, the blue pencils can be digitally removed in photoshop.

The Many Faces of Fowler

Dr. Julius Fowler's likeness has been realized by many artists on the Rare Earth Comics team. The artists going clockwise from the upper left are: Antonio Negron, David Robles, Antonio Negron again & Jeff Tingley.